Little footprints

Who's digging in the Garden?

Colouring and activities for caring kids

Whose bushy tail is this?

Why is our little brown book so very, very green?

The cover of this Little Footprints book is made from 100% virgin pulp from a sustainable forest. The colouring and activity pages inside are made from 100% recycled fibre paper. Both are very environmentally friendly.

Where are the gardens?

Gardens give food and shelter to thousands of animals and insects.

Colour the gardens green.
Draw a map of a garden you know.

Animals and insects keep gardens alive.

Who's in the garden?

day-old butterflies

hungry caterpillar

soil-sucking earthworms

Draw more animals and insects.

berry-eating birds

Who else has been in the garden?

honey-making bees

hard-working ants

Under stones...

A brown centipede hides under a stone during the day – beware its poisonous head claws.

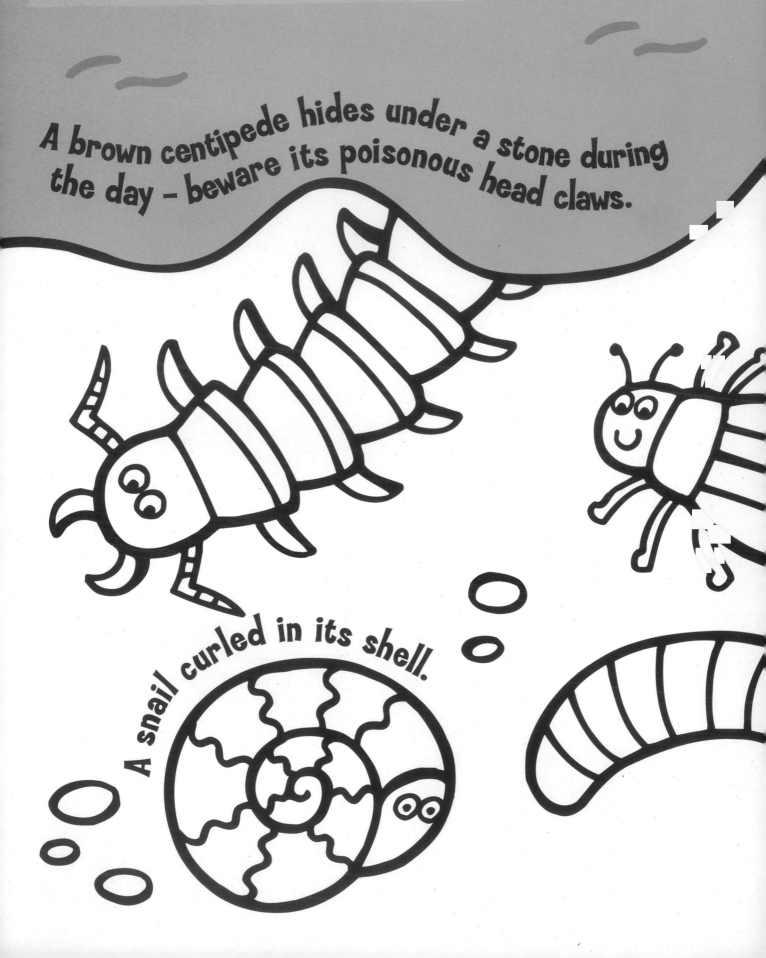

A snail curled in its shell.

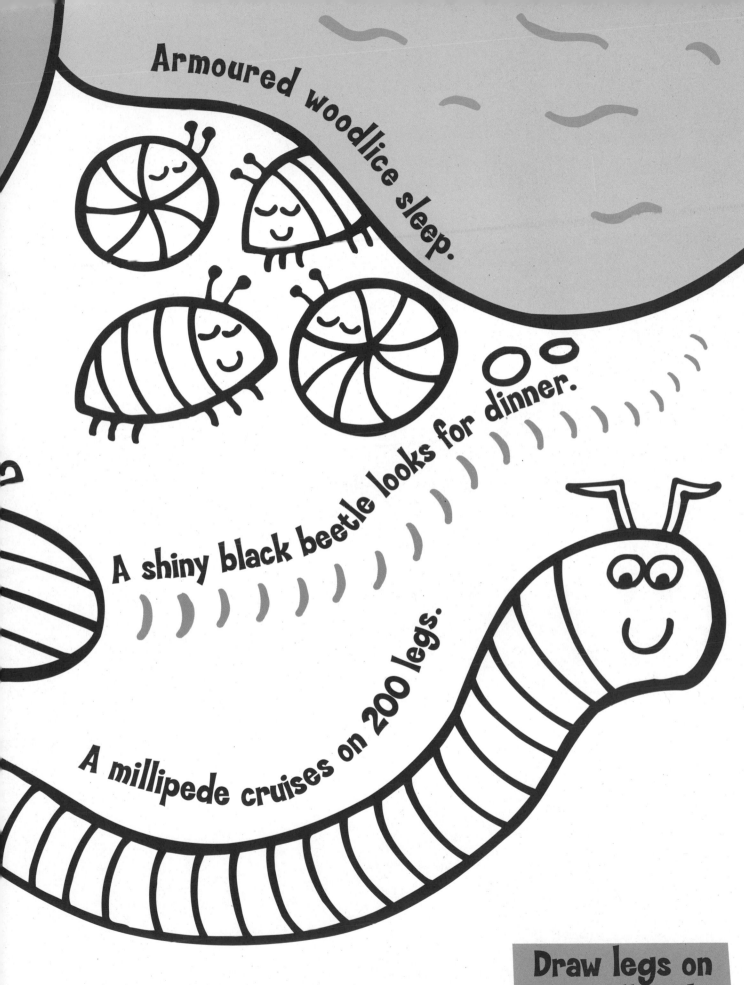

Armoured woodlice sleep.

A shiny black beetle looks for dinner.

A millipede cruises on 200 legs.

Draw legs on the millipede.

In shrubs and trees...

Birds sing from tree-tops – the dawn chorus.

A mosquito looks for a victim.

Tiny weevils make holes in leaves.

In the pond...

Frogspawn – like jelly, floats near the surface.

Draw more wriggling tadpoles.

Water snails twist and turn.

A dragonfly hovers over the water...

... while pond skaters walk on it!

A water boatman does the backstroke.

The male newt looks like a tiny dragon.

In the soil...

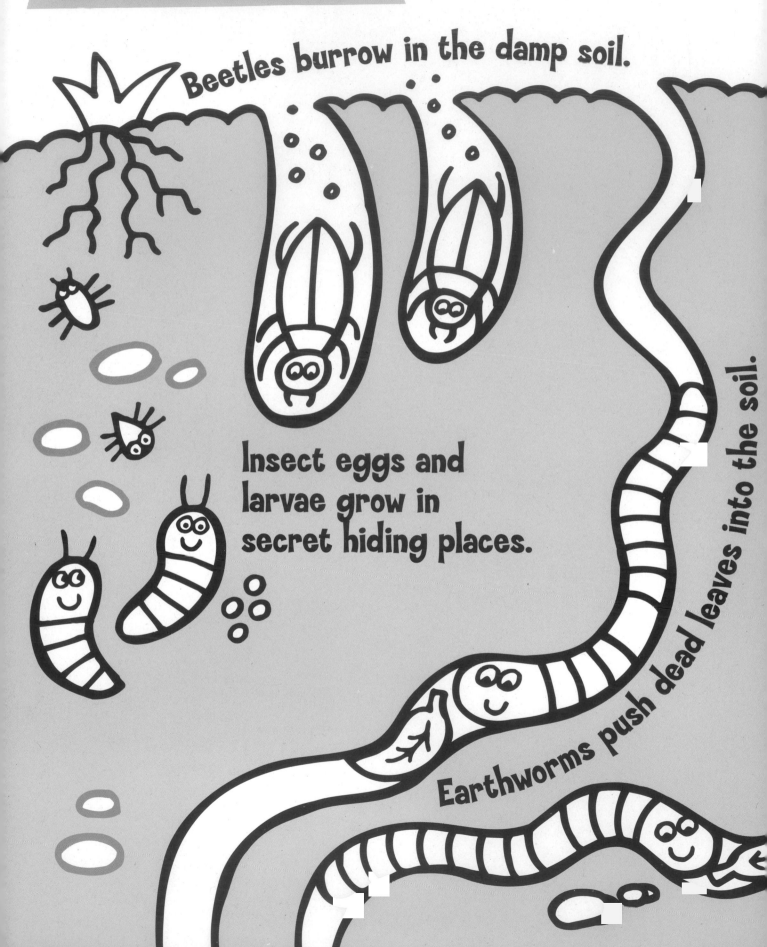

Beetles burrow in the damp soil.

Insect eggs and larvae grow in secret hiding places.

Earthworms push dead leaves into the soil.

When no one's looking,
a garden spider spins
a sticky web.

Who's digging?

The vole is digging and...

... so is mole.

The thrush is digging for worms.

What's in the compost?

Things that decay make good soil in which plants can grow.

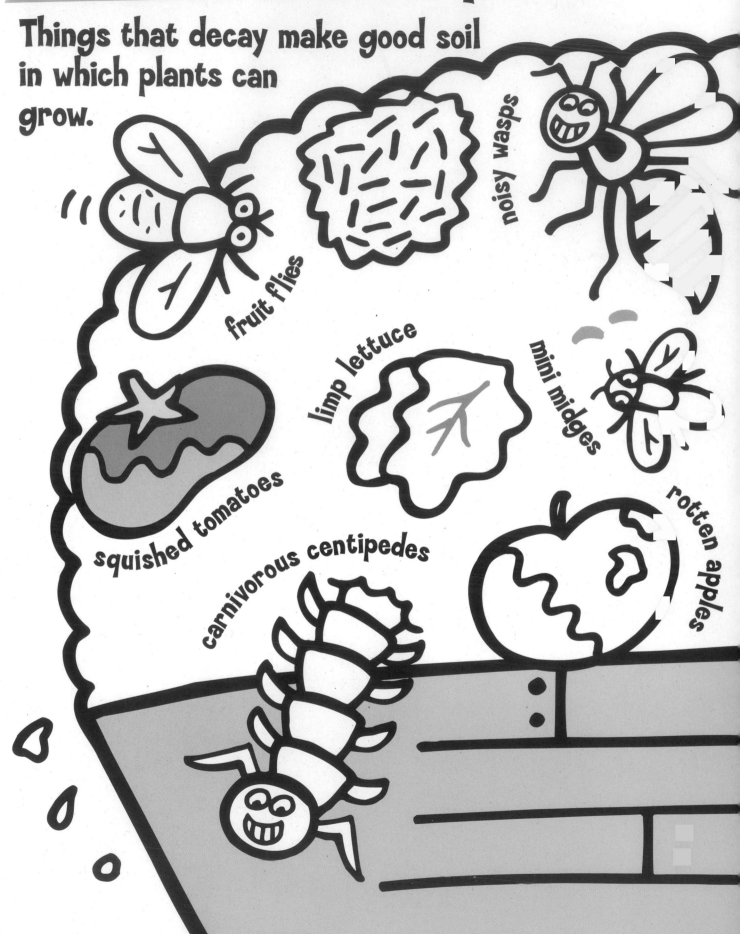

fruit flies

noisy wasps

limp lettuce

mini midges

squished tomatoes

carnivorous centipedes

rotten apples

In the dustbin...

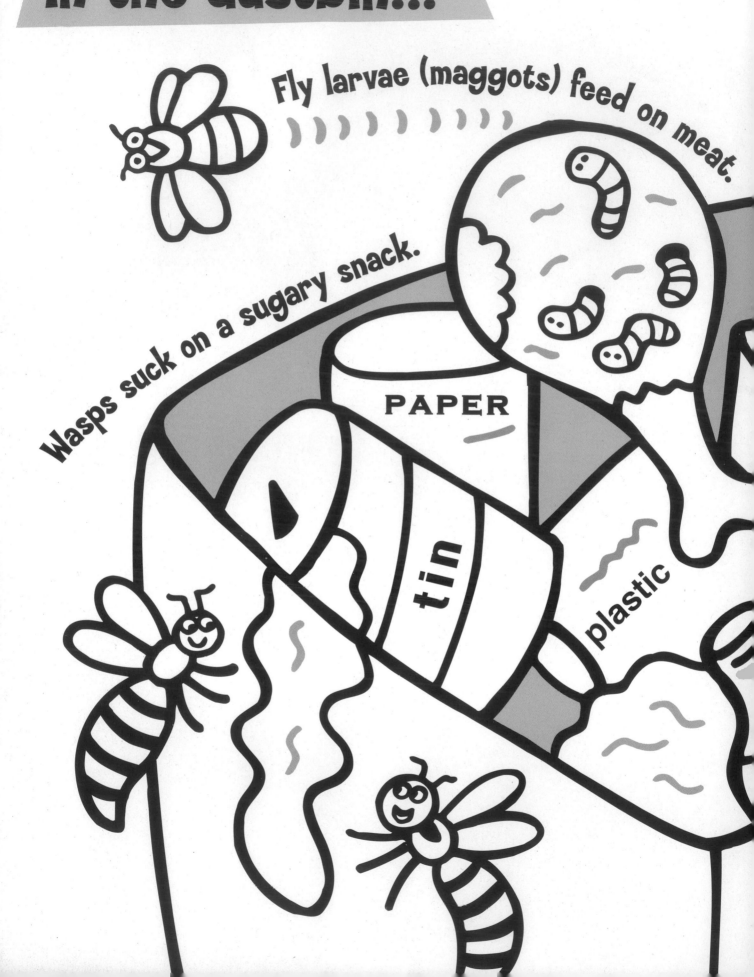

Fly larvae (maggots) feed on meat.

Wasps suck on a sugary snack.

PAPER

tin

plastic

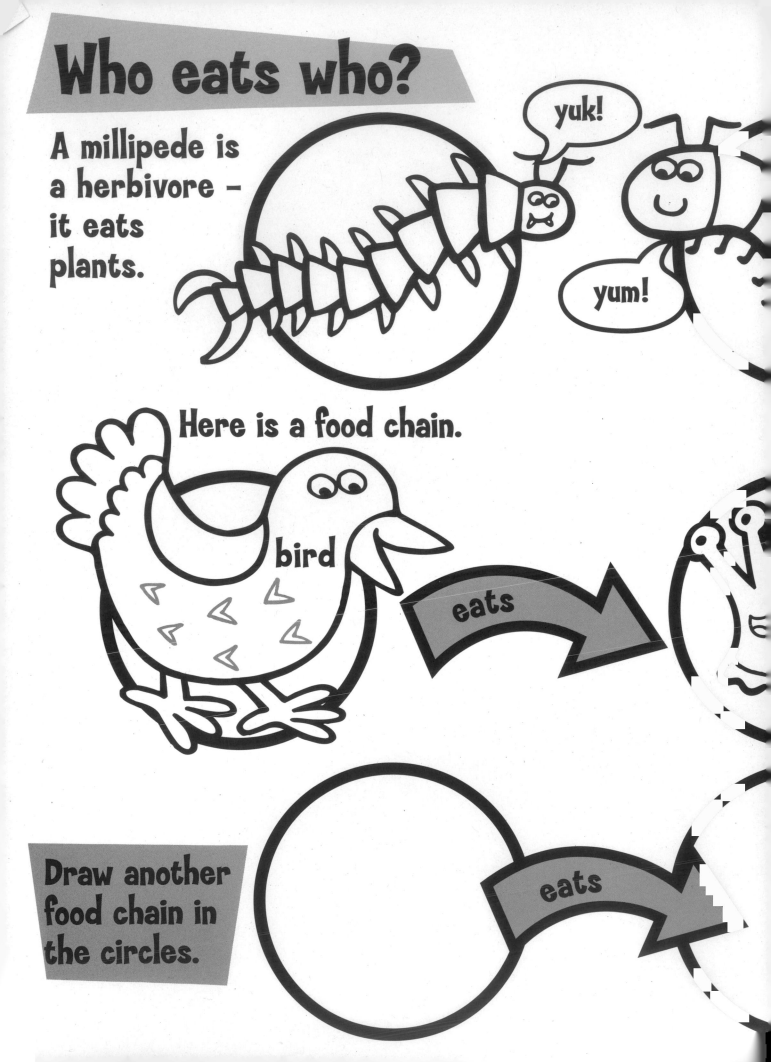

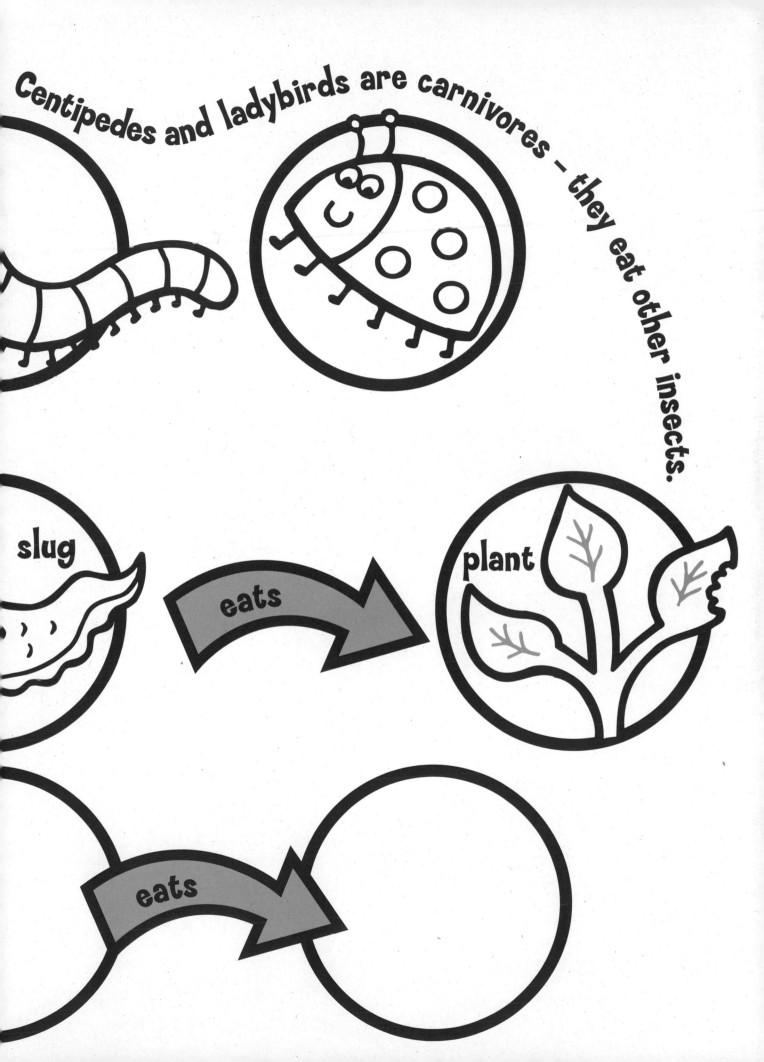

Centipedes and ladybirds are carnivores – they eat other insects.

slug

plant

eats

eats

What's happening in spring?

egg

caterpillar

Learn the life cycle of a butterfly.

chrysalis

butterfly

The male bird sings to attract a mate.

Baby birds are growing inside these eggs.

The mayfly lives for just one day!

In the summer....

Butterflies stick out their long proboscis to slurp nectar from flowers.

Find the colony of ants. Can you see the nursery where soldier ants guard cocoons?

Brightly coloured flowers attract birds and insects.

Blow a dandelion clock. Where the seeds fall, dandelions will grow.

Pollen sticks like dust to the bees' furry bodies.

In the autumn...

Seeds are blown by the wind.

Mushrooms and toadstools pop up!

A frog finds somewhere to hibernate.

Squirrels gather acorns.

Shiny brown conkers plop on the ground.

A female spider wraps her eggs in a silky bundle.

Blackbirds steal orange berries.

In the winter...

... there are things you can do to help the animals.

Leave food and water for the birds.

Do not disturb the frog hibernating under a rock.

Don't use all the berries to decorate the halls!

Don't touch squirrel's secret store of nuts.

Don't turn over old leaves. They could be a duvet for a hedgehog.

Little footprints in action!

THE BIRDS AND THE BEES
Attract bees and butterflies into the garden by planting flowers. Although a butterfly may lay 100 eggs, only two or three will live to become butterflies. In spring, put up a nest box for blue tits. Scatter nuts and seeds on a covered feeder and have fresh water nearby for all feathered winter visitors.

THE HOLLY AND THE IVY
Plant trees and shrubs that offer food and protection for your garden guests. Ivy provides good cover for all kinds of creatures. It has flowers and berries, too.

LET THE GRASS GROW!
Have a wild area in the garden. Let the grass grow long so that it attracts and houses a wide variety of wildlife.

FLOWER POWER
Grow insect-loving flowers such as forget-me-not, nasturtiums, honeysuckle, lilac, clover, buddleia, clematis and lavender.

RECIPE FOR HOME-MADE COMPOST:
A compost heap is a habitat for lots of different creatures that all help to break down the waste turning it into rich soil.
Ask an adult to help with this project.
- Layer potato peelings, grass cuttings, tea bags, leftover vegetables, lettuce, eggshells and fruit.
- Add scraps of newspaper and cardboard.
- Sprinkle with water and stir with a garden fork to let in air.
- Cover with a plastic sheet or carpet.
- Leave to rot for about six months.
Don't put onions, cooked food, meat or fish on the compost heap – the worms don't like them and they will attract vermin!

GARDEN SAFARI
When in a garden or park, keep a picture and word diary of what you see. For example: draw and colour different types of leaves and label them; or draw a young plant then measure it regularly to see how fast it grows.